~~THE LOSER~~ UNDERVALUED UNTIL THEY SUCCEED

Rini Murarka

INDIA · SINGAPORE · MALAYSIA

ISBN 979-8-89186-864-9

CONTENTS

Contents

PART – SECOND

Contents

PART -THIRD

PART - ONE

1

A FIGHTER FROM BIRTH

"Good news!! She survived!" The doctor exclaimed.

Everyone smiled.

A girl named Joanne was sleeping. She was 3 years old and was at her grandmother's place with her mother Mrs. Clara. It was a hot and sunny afternoon. Mrs. Clara covered her with a thin blanket and went to bring some official papers of their shop to finish the work while the grandmother went to the restroom. While returning, Granny saw the working ceiling fan fall right next to Joanne. Though the fan missed her, her hand got severely cut from the fan's blade and she got badly injured. She lost a lot of blood and fainted.

Mr. Jack was Joanne's uncle. Mrs. Clara told everything to him. He asked her to rush to the hospital. The doctors there, after analyzing her, told her that she needed AB-negative blood to replace whatever she had lost. Her blood group was rare and no one in the family had that blood group. So, Uncle Jack took her to another hospital in a different city. As he was a doctor, he had other doctor friends in that hospital. And coincidentally one of his friends had the same blood group which she needed. She cried a lot because of the pain. The doctors started treating her. It was difficult for Mrs. Clara to see Joanne in such pain but she couldn't do anything. It took 3-4 days to heal her partially, but the doctors gave a sigh of relief.

Joanne was discharged from the hospital and the injuries took months to heal.

Everyone returned and gave the utmost care to her and felt relieved that she was getting better.

2

LITTLE INNOCENT JOANNE

06:45 AM

Monday

Joanne was 6 years old. She took a bath and got ready for school. Mrs. Clara gave her milk and cornflakes to eat and dropped her at the school. Joanne was very small at that time. She reached her class very early and she started to cry when she noticed her classroom door was closed. After a while, someone came in, opened the door, and she entered.

Little Joanne was sweet and very innocent. If to laugh at, her innocence level was at its peak. Even if she prepared for the tests and exams, she would forget everything. She would even forget her ABCs and would copy from her friend.

Poor Joanne!

Mrs. Clara always wanted her to repeat one class as she thought she got an early admission. So she requested the teachers to make her repeat the class. But she always passed her exams and the teachers rejected her request.

But, this request of Mrs. Clara worked tragically when she failed her 12th exams and her mother's request to repeat one class worked at the wrong time.

Shit happened with Joanne and Mrs. Clara!

Well, not to laugh, and a year passed.

Though she grew older, she did not grow in height.

It was morning time at school and every student came to class and settled down. The teacher came in and asked to make a queue as they had to go to the assembly hall for the morning prayer. Everyone gathered outside the class and started making the queue, Joanne thought of standing between her friends.

"Joanne!" the teacher called out.

"Yes ma'am," Joanne replied.

"Come to the front," the teacher said.

"Ok ma'am," Joanne replied.

She moved to the front of the queue and then she said to herself, "Why do I have to stand in front of the queue every time even though I don't know where I have to go? Why am I so short?"

Coincidentally, all her friends were taller than her.

And this keeps happening every time!

3

PIN-DROP SILENCE

Class 1

Morning Prayer

It was a usual day at the school. Joanne and her friends gathered near the door of the class and were talking with some friends. Suddenly, they realized that the teacher was about to come and prayer was about to start and everyone went back to their seats. But the students were chattering away at their seats and the class monitor started to monitor the class.

"Hey! Keep quiet!" Smith said.

Smith was the monitor of the class.

He went near each and every student and asked them to stay quiet.

Everyone stopped chatting.

The prayer was about to start and everyone was asked to stand up. Smith kept monitoring the class as the teacher had not arrived till then. Some of the students did not stand up from their seats as chit-chat was still going on and they didn't hear the bell. Some students were so naughty that they did it for fun.

Smith went to each and every student and asked them to stand up. He asked Joanne to stand up for the prayer and hit her on the elbow with a ruler.

She didn't hear the prayer bell, so she stood up for the prayer after being hit.

When the prayer was about to end, Joanne started to feel dizzy and she fell on the floor. Everyone was shocked and by then the teacher had arrived.

"Hey! Get up! Get up! What happened?" Joanne's classmate asked.

The voices were echoing around her, someone sprinkled water on her face and she slowly started to regain her senses. While trying to open her eyes, she realized that everyone was gathered around her. She felt a bit ashamed. Someone gave her water and then she sat on the seat.

She wondered how and why she fainted.

Joanne did realize that Smith hit her for no reason, but she didn't tell her parents.

4

CUNNING FRIEND

Wednesday Morning

7:10 AM

Joanne and Linda were classmates but not very good friends.

It was a regular day and the first class had just gotten over. Everyone stood from their seats and started to roam around the class. Joanne and Linda were standing near the door of the class. Some conversation started between the two and it got so heated up that Linda twisted Joanne's hand and held it against her back just to tease her.

Suddenly the bell rang and Linda and Joanne went back to their seats. The teacher came in soon after that.

Joanne didn't understand what had happened!

Joanne was hurt by the incident.

Later, when they moved into higher grades, Linda, and Joanne became good friends. But Linda was quite a dominating and cunning girl and Joanne never ever understood this thing.

5

CARELESS JOANNE

Class 1

07:30 am

Exam time

Joanne was preparing for an exam and she had done it thoroughly.

The next morning when she reached her class, her classmates were discussing something about the paper. During the discussion, she thought, 'Shit! I studied something else!'

Joanne suddenly went blank!!

The bell rang!!!

Everyone sat down to attend the exam. As the teacher was distributing the question paper, she became quite nervous. She held the paper in her hand and started to read it and the very next moment she realized she didn't remember anything

She wrote the exam with a blank mind, unaware of what she wrote.

When the results came, she knew she must have flunked and she did.

Cheers to Joanne for studying the wrong subject at the right time.

MOTHER – THE SAVIORS

She did the same thing one more time. She was studying and preparing for the exams. Suddenly, Mrs. Clara went to the terrace and she was talking to the neighbor. The neighbor's son was in Joanne's batch but not in the same section. Mrs. Clara was having a normal conversation and they started talking about the chapters and suddenly, she mentioned the subject.

Mrs. Clara realized Joanne was studying the wrong subject.

Careless Joanne!!

Mrs. Clara asked, "What are you studying? What exam do you have tomorrow?"

She told her about the exam.

Mrs. Clara asked, "Did you even check the timetable?"

She said, "No."

"As expected, how can you even do that? You are so careless. You should check before studying. At least, one must paste the timetable near your study table. But, no, you are overconfident," her mother scolded.

"Sorry mom," she replied.

And then she went into her room and started preparing for her exam and Mrs. Clara turned out to be her embarrassment savior.

6

A WIN-WIN TURNED INTO NO WIN

Joanne was 13 years old. Mrs. Clara always wanted her to do something meaningful with life. After all, whose parents don't? She did a lot for her studies. With that, Mrs. Clara enrolled her in many extra-curricular classes.

She took singing classes at a music school. They also taught dance and musical instruments. There was an event being conducted for singing and dancing, and several music schools participated in that.

Each school selected their best student to participate and represent their school, Joanne didn't know all this. Her music teacher told her to participate in the events. The music teacher felt that she could sing well and added her name to the list of participants. She started working hard on her and she just did what her teacher told her. Her teacher told Mrs. Clara that she was participating in a competition at the school and Mrs. Clara got very excited. For Joanne, she didn't think about anything, she was extremely normal. She didn't give any thought for any performance or about representing her school.

It didn't even hit her that she was representing or doing something on stage. She did all the things in an extremely casual way.

It was her competition day. Her music teacher called Mrs. Clara on the phone and asked her to make Joanne rehearse the song 2-3 times.

When Mrs. Clara asked Joanne to rehearse the song, she simply replied, "I did it, Mum. Now, I am not going to do it again."

In short, she lied that she had rehearsed it and went for the competition without rehearsals.

The program started at 2 and ended at 8 PM. There were several performances and many performances were great. She participated in two: one in a group performance and another in a solo. She did her performance and came back to her seat. After all the performances, the judges started to announce the results. It was 7 by then and she was very tired, but her music teacher wanted to wait till the results were out.

In the end, during prize distribution time, her name was announced as the 3rd rank in solo performance, and even her group performance also won some prizes. She was more than happy.

Joanne's cousin's brother came to pick her up from the event. He saw her prize and he twisted it so hard that it broke. Joanne got upset but didn't say anything.

She went home and cried and showed it to Mrs. Clara. Mrs. Clara told her, "He didn't do this purposely, Joanne.

He did it by mistake. It's okay, what matters is that you won a prize in the competition and we are so proud of this."

Her music teacher asked her to bring the prize to her music class so that she could see it. Joanne kept on making excuses out of embarrassment and she never took the prize to show it to her.

It was the first prize in her life that she earned from her talent and even that broke.

Our mind plays with us all the time. It's on us how it should be tackled. Joanne never knew the competition, representing her music school, stage fear, and other things. She did it very casually. Even her music teacher had the utmost faith in her and she bloomed.

Each and every child is special, if people try to understand them, then their situation becomes easier and they start to bloom.

7

SOMEONE REALLY UNDERSTOOD HER

THE ROXANNE MA'AM

CLASS 4TH

Roxanne ma'am was checking the attendance of the class after the morning prayer. After that, she just wanted to appreciate the children for their hard work.

"Stand up, Joanne," Roxanne ma'am said.

"Yes ma'am," Joanne replied.

"She got 72% in exams, please clap everyone!!" Roxanne ma'am announced in class.

And the class was filled with the sound of claps.

"Thank you," Joanne said.

It was a very small incident for others but for Joanne it was something special. Joanne never forgot that teacher in her whole life. Every student is different, teachers need to understand more about students and what Roxanne ma'am did was she tried to understand that Joanne was a bit slow. And sometimes, some children can really do well if they are treated with love. If she asks more than twice, she gets scolded, or they think she is not paying attention to the problem, but she takes time to understand any particular thing.

Everyone was hard on her as if she didn't want to study and would start to scold her. Only a few handled her lovingly. So, slowly she stopped asking her doubts to teachers because either some would scold her or they would make her feel embarrassed in front of other students which damaged her confidence. But with Roxanne ma'am, she could freely ask doubts as many times as she wanted.

Joanne never got more than 65% or 67% but this 4% increase in her percent meant a lot for her. More than anything, someone tried to understand her and pushed her.

Those who really understand her do not stay long with her, they transfer to some other city, like Roxanne mam got transferred in a different city.

8

DUTY IN CHARGE

Generally, what happens is the whole class gets an opportunity to be in charge of managing any lobby area in front of the classes. The whole list of students was displayed with names and details on the notice board and this time Joanne got an opportunity to manage it for a week.

She got the duty to stand in front of the 2nd class during the morning prayer and in the afternoon as well. At 7:00 am sharp, she stood in front of 2nd class. Her job was to make sure each student was in the class before the prayer started and if the teacher was late before the prayer, she had to make sure that the whole class was silent. In the afternoon, before the last bell, the duty in charge had to make sure after the last bell, each and every student went in line to exit the gate of the school, and she did really well.

Though the role was small, for Joanne it was something special as it boosted her confidence and made her happy.

9

THE REGULAR FIGHT

SATURDAY

08:00 PM

Joanne had a half-day at school. Joanne and her brother Jankie were watching TV in their room in the evening. Suddenly, some noise came from their father's shop. They both ran to see what happened. Their father was shouting into the phone and the argument escalated quickly. The staff had misplaced the official papers of the products from the shop and went home. He was searching for that paper, but he couldn't find it. So he called the staff and instead of listening and making that person understand, he yelled a lot. Joanne & Jankie went back and started doing their regular stuff. They packed their bags according to the timetable and then went to sleep.

The next morning, the staff came and gave the paper to him from where he kept it.

But with all the yelling, they got furious and were quite tense seeing this as their father was short-tempered.

10

HUGE EMBARRASSMENT

CLASS 7

11:30 AM

It was the History test day. After that it was recess. Joanne prepared for it completely. The teacher came in and announced that everyone had to do their final preparations. Then, after fifteen minutes, she gave the question handouts to everyone.

The teacher divided all the students and gave them a time limit. Joanne forgot some answers but whatever she knew, she wrote. Joanne, after finishing her test, started to help one of her classmates. The physics teacher caught her but didn't say anything to her as the bell rang for recess and everyone submitted the paper. He was having his class again after the recess.

They had their lunch during recess. When the physics teacher came in after the recess got over, he asked Joanne to stand up and started throwing all the questions which were given in the test. She got terrified and she couldn't answer anything. Her teacher embarrassed her and scolded her and then she sat. She went home and cried a lot. It hurt her a lot.

Every student is different, so maybe public embarrassment was not good for her. If he wanted to scold her, he could ask her privately to come and make her understand. It deeply devastated her confidence.

11

CYNTHIA

Cynthia was a tall, slim, and dusky girl. Her nature was quite similar to Joanne's; silent, introverted, good at making friends, and average in studies. She joined this school from the 3rd grade. Before that, she was living with her relatives in a big and different city and she was studying there only. She was very clear with her goal from the start that she would be a model. She didn't like to study much and she was very clear and straight about it.

Cynthia and Joanne shared the same class but they did not have the same sections. They shared a common tuition center and became friends. They were in class 7 when they became good friends. Both of them struggled with their studies and had no confidence. Whenever they had a problem, they would talk to each other. The funny thing is they both didn't have the best solution either.

Joanne didn't share everything with her mother as she was not that free with her. Even Cynthia shared most of the things with Joanne only. Maybe because she thought Joanne would understand her better.

They spent most of the time together whenever they had free time and they talked on calls a lot. They shared everything with each other. Joanne didn't like to share problems related to her family with anyone. She just felt that she didn't want anyone to think that anyone in her family was bad or her family had such fights. Basically, she doesn't want her family to be judged by others. She just felt it was her family and any problem in her family should be kept to herself because even if anyone was wrong among her parents, they were her parents and she couldn't hear a single word against either of them.

Whenever it was exam time, they would discuss, and prepare together.

Slowly, everyone knew they were best friends.

12

INFLUENCED FIGHT

SUNDAY

06:00 PM

The grandparents came to meet Joanne's parents and children as they don't live together. Joanne and Jankie came down from upstairs, and they both got really excited after seeing them. Everyone talked a bit to Grandpa. Then her mother asked them to come to the dinner table, and they had dinner together. Joanne and her brother went upstairs after saying goodnight to their grandparents. Grandpa started to tell some things to her father and after a while, they both went home.

What happened next?

Joanne's father started questioning her mother.

He asked, "Why did you go there with them? Why did you do this?"

And without listening to the answers, he started shouting which turned into a raging argument and that turned into a fight out of nowhere.

The noises of the parents fighting could be heard in Joanne's room. They didn't understand the reason for the fight and it scared them.

Mother started crying and with that, she slept. Everyone was worried and slept in a bad mood that day.

13

COZY NOZY

NEXT DAY

Joanne and Jankie went to school, the same stuff happened at school. After returning from school, they freshened up, changed their clothes, took some rest, had lunch, and then went for their tuition. Jankie went to roam with his friends after the tuition class, and Joanne's two friends Maxwell and Adam showed up at her home. Her best friend Cynthia was also there. Joanne went into the kitchen to reheat the pizza for her friends which she ordered from the restaurant. Cynthia was talking with them in the room. She came into the room with pizza.

Maxwell had a crush on Joanne and she too liked him. They all ate pizza and went to wash their hands. Joanne showed the way to the restroom. After washing their hands, she was standing near the wall. Maxwell kept both his hands on the wall and covered her, he came closer towards her face and tried to kiss her. But Joanne was not ready for it. She just escaped towards the living room towards her mother where she saw her parents were having some kind of argument. Mrs. Clara asked her to go back to the room, but deep within she understood that something was wrong. She went back to the room and after some time her friends went off.

Joanne was terrified and upset.

14

TIGHT SLAP – SENSITIVE HEART

WEDNESDAY

08:00 AM

It was the first period of the day. The class teacher was taking the attendance of the class after the prayer time. While taking attendance, she called Joanne to the front of the class and asked her to remove the spectacles. As she removed it, the class teacher gave her a tight slap on her cheeks and then she asked her to wear the spectacles and to stand outside the classroom.

She slapped her just for being absent for one day. Even her mother called the teacher a day before to inform her about the leave. She got her periods and she was in pain which is why Joanne took leave.

For a while, Joanne was blank, but then she felt humiliated and embarrassed.

Teachers need to understand their students. They need to maintain teacher-student relations before teaching them.

Small things really make a disastrous impact on a child's mind, and that too on a sensitive child.

15

ONE MARK

CLASS 8TH

MARKS SHOWING DAY

The teacher distributed the answer sheet of the civics paper to everyone. After a while, she asked all the students who got less than 5 marks out of 10 to stand up. Three students stood up out of which Joanne was one of them.

"1 mark in civics. Who is this?" Sussanne ma'am asked.

Joanne felt embarrassed as she knew it was her.

"What happened, Joanne?" Sussanne ma'am asked.

She kept quiet.

"In the whole class, only you got 1 mark. Improve, Joanne. Otherwise, it will be very difficult for you. Work hard."

Joanne sat down after that.

It was recess time. She was eating her lunch while sitting on the concrete bench with her friend. Suddenly, she heard some conversation of her classmates about how a girl got 1 mark in civics behind her. The girls who were talking behind Joanne didn't notice that she was sitting in front of her.

Joanne felt more embarrassed.

Joanne went home and cried.

Poor Joanne! She studies a lot, but she forgets things easily.

16

FUNNY NAMES

If someone teased Joanne with funny names, it used to hurt her. It hurts her when her cousin or anyone else talks about her height or studies to tease her.

She really thought, 'Why don't people understand that if someone is teasing her, it hurts her feelings too?'

Maybe, it stayed in their mind forever. She thought, 'Words are magic, if we use them correctly, they will have a positive impact.'

Sometimes, her cousin teases her with the words like little Joanne, fatso Joanne etc. For some, it wouldn't bother them, but for a childlike Joanne, it pierced inside the soul slowly, slowly, and slowly.

It shattered her confidence completely.

17

ACCIDENT

HOME

08:30 PM

Joanne was having dinner when her father came from somewhere. He changed his clothes and started talking to her mother about his shop and other things. Eventually, it turned into a fight and her father took the car and went somewhere out of anger. At first, her mother thought he would come after a while. But he didn't return even after a long time and she called some of his friends and asked about him. When he didn't show up even after several hours, she got really worried. Later her father called and said that he met with an accident and got badly hurt near his eyes. He came home, driving on his own with one eye injured, and then they went to the hospital. The eyelid of one eye was badly injured, and the doctor bandaged it up. It took months to heal.

But, the fights were so regular in Joanne's family that even a loud voice scared her and her mother as well.

18

TWO SECTIONS

CLASS 10TH

Joanne's school had two sections for each class.

In class 10th, both sections were divided on the basis of percentage: above 60 percent and below 60 percent. Basically, it was done to focus more on weaker students.

It must be obvious by now that Joanne was below 60 percent and her best friend Cynthia from another section also fell in the same section. The first assessment exam was finally over and the teachers were coming to show the answer sheets to the students. It was math class. The teacher started to distribute the paper and Joanne got good marks. Her best friend Cynthia saw that at one place she didn't get the marks, then they both went to the teacher for correction.

The teacher said that Joanne was given marks by mistake and deducted them. After coming back to the seats, Joanne started to yell at Cynthia for this. Later, she realized she got the wrong marks and they both burst into laughter. Even Cynthia felt bad. She thought it would increase her marks, but the opposite happened.

Joanne and her stories were seriously amazing.

THIS SCHOOL WAS TILL HIGH SCHOOL.

SHE CLEARED HER 10TH WITH SO-CALLED AVERAGE MARKS OF 65 PERCENT.

HIGH SCHOOL OVER.

19

NEW SCHOOL

NEW SCHOOL

11TH AND 12TH

NEW CLASSMATES WITH SOME OLD FRIENDS.

Cynthia was with her. Her last school was the best and the talk of the town. Everyone was jealous of them because of the last school. 7 girls made a group as they were from the same school and eventually, the backbenchers boys group was also formed. Almost all the time, there was some sort of fight among these two groups.

There was a boy named Sebastian in the boys' group. During English class, all the students were talking. Suddenly, the teacher came and saw that some guys in class were laughing and then pointed to one guy named Sebastian to stand. Then the teacher asked, "What are you talking and laughing about?" He kept quiet.

The teacher asked again.

He stayed quiet.

Then the teacher shouted.

He frustratingly replied, "ma'am, her size is literally like a watermelon." The whole class went quiet.

The teacher took Sebastian to the Principal's office and he was suspended for a week.

And when Sara saw her after the class, she gave Sebastian a tight slap.

What he literally meant was her boobs were actually the size of a watermelon.

20

NAUGHTINESS AT ITS PEAK

The girl gang became so naughty that they finished their lunch before lunch time. Then they make a ball of aluminum foil which they bought in their lunch box to wrap their food and start to target inside the trash one by one.

Getting scolded by the teacher was a casual thing for them.

Recess was over and Economics class started.

Victor sir came in and started teaching. Suddenly, the English teacher came in to ask something and all the students in the class started talking to each other. Victor sir asked everyone to stay quiet. All the students stayed quiet for a few minutes and then, they started talking again. Seeing this, Victor sir asked Cynthia along with 3-4 girls near her to stand up as they all were talking a lot. After scolding everyone, Victor sir said, "You all don't have manners, two teachers are standing here and instead of respecting us, you all are busy gossiping. You should be a role model for others."

Cynthia replied slowly, "Firstly, I should be a model, only then will I get the roles, huh?"

But, the teacher didn't listen to this and threw them out of the class and a few boys as well.

Things really got worse.

While they were standing outside the class, Joanne started to peep into another class which was next to their class and the teacher noticed it. She came outside and slapped all the girls for their naughtiness. She sent the whole group of girls to the principal's office.

All the girls got really worried because of this.

The 5 boys were having fun seeing all this but one of them went to the teacher and requested on their behalf. He was that teacher's favorite. At first, he got scolded by the teacher but he requested once again. To which, the teacher gave a warning and asked them to go back to their classes.

All the girls felt embarrassed while entering the class and they went back to their seats.

21

FLUNKED AND SPOTTED

Everyone was a piece in Joanne's group. Kalen was extremely slim and used to wear extremely loose school dresses. She wasn't very naughty in class, but she used to bring her cell phone which she generally keeps in her socks and used to go to the restroom to call her boyfriend. She goes to the restroom with Cynthia most of the time.

In all the naughtiness, Joanne topped in accounts in 11th, but she badly flunked in 12th. The situation at her home was not so good and she was very distracted. Even Cynthia flunked as well.

Only Kalen cleared.

Everyone else failed at least in one subject.

Cynthia and Joanne flunked in 2-3 subjects.

A year setback.

Both of them were devastated

It took time for them to heal, it felt like a culprit for them to get stuck.

When the result came out, Joanne was at her granny's place, and her uncle scolded her. Even her father, brother, and mother cried because of the result.

Joanne went to have breakfast after the 12th result came out and her uncle and mother were sitting right there on the dining table and having their breakfast. She was feeling horrible from the inside and started to have her breakfast. Her uncle said to her in front of Joanne's mother,

"As expected, you won't be able to do any good with your life."

She stayed quiet, finished her breakfast and went into Granny's room straightaway.

Joanne generally forgets everything in life, but this line stuck to her heart forever.

But she really worked hard and cleared the 12th Std.

But it was a spot on her academics forever!

Cynthia cleared it too!

They both got admissions to different places and their routes were set apart, but they were connected through phone.

Cynthia did textile designing and Joanne continued a professional course with normal grades.

She was 19, but she was unable to love herself as anyone could come and say something about her height knowingly or unknowingly. She was average in her studies, so everyone saw her like that. She was not smart, witty, fast, or beautiful. She was being compared for each and everything in her life with someone.

She started to hate herself and each and every one pointed out her mistakes repeatedly. It became really hard for her to flourish.

She rarely heard any good comments about her and she still kept on pursuing higher studies.

PART – SECOND

THE NEXT PHASE

Joanne daydreamed a lot and loved to watch movies (Hollywood romantic, real incident-based, and biographical movies). She really thought college life would be like how it was shown in the movies. But her experience was the opposite of it. Relationships are not like what is shown in movies. She thought the cute moments that the couple spent happened in real life too and things moved on!

Joanne never knew what she wanted to do. Her lack of clarity made her mother take the decision on her behalf. She took the grads course and applied for professional courses with that.

She tried in two cities, one, where her cousin was studying and another place, which is good for preparing for professional exams. Joanne and her cousin were in the same class, but they both lived in different cities.

Her mother decided that she would take the admission which was good for professional exams. She moved to another city for further studies, where she started the next chapter of her life. Joanne's mother came with her to help her settle for college and a place to live.

While taking admission to her college, she met some new people in her class out of which she became friends with two people. They both were trying to find a place to live in the new city with their parents.

Joanne and her mother were searching for a room to stay. They saw many places. Coincidentally, she met with her college mates again while searching for it and they saw many places together. The whole day passed, but they could not decide on a place.

The next day, Joanne, and her mother went to a place and they both liked it. She talked to the owner, and everything was good, and she finalized it.

After settling her, mother went home, and Joanne started her new life being very scared.

1

NEW CITY – OLD FRIEND

10 PM

IN BED

PG

"Hello!" Joanne answered after her phone rang.

"Hi, Joanne. How are you?" he asked.

"I am good, missing everyone. How are you?" Joanne asked.

"Great! Great! Are you excited for college?" he asked.

"More than excitement, I am scared and nervous," she answered.

"Well, everything will go great. Stay positive," he consoled her.

"Thank you, Leo. Miss you," she said.

"Miss you too. At what time is your college going to start?" he asked.

"The first class will start at 06:30 am," she replied.

"Then you should sleep early, right?" he asked.

"Yeah!" she said.

"How far is your college and how will you go?" he asked.

"10 minutes by bus," she replied.

"OK. Let's talk tomorrow and sleep on time. OK?" he said.

"Yeah," she replied.

"I will also do the assignment work for college tomorrow and will sleep then. Ok. Goodnight Joan… Tc," he said.

"Good night, Leo. Take care," she answered.

Leo was her friend from class 12. Their friendship started when class 12th ended and he got her number from his friend's phone with whom Joanne was having friendship. He took her number secretly.

One day, he texted her, and they started to chit-chat. Generally, they talk only at night. She was in her hometown as she was preparing for 12th again and he was in college doing graduation. They talked on a daily basis after that for a year. And, as she cleared 12th, she went out for further studies.

Joanne really had some feelings for him, she wanted him to propose to her. He also liked her, but he didn't want to spoil the friendship with her for the sake of a relationship.

Joanne desperately wanted to have a boyfriend as in teenage, everyone was having one. But she never had one.

They continued to chit-chat on text and on calls after moving out.

2
IVY

6:15 AM

BUS STOP

"Hi!" Ivy said.

"Hello," Joanne replied.

"Are you going to City College?" Ivy asked.

"Yes. What about you?" Joanne asked.

"Same college. What course?" Ivy asked.

"Bachelor of Commerce. What are your subjects?" Joanne replied.

"Accounts, Business, Economics and so on," Ivy replied.

"Same subjects. We are classmates then. Where do you stay?" Joanne asked.

"Folsom Street. And you?" Ivy asked.

"Howard Street. We both can go to college together," Joanne said.

"Oh nice, I will wait here for you from tomorrow," she replies.

"Great!" Joanne said.

Ivy was from that city only and she lived with her family. She lived with her mother and two sisters. She also had a boyfriend of another religion. Her financial condition was weak and she helped her mother in her family business. They became very good friends, sat together, ate together, and studied together. They shared all their secrets with each other. They spent most of their time together in college. When Joanne felt alone or bored, she went to Ivy's place and sometimes even stayed with her.

3

SNEAKY PEAKY TEXT

08:30 PM

PAYING GUEST

TEXT CHAT

"Hi. I got the number from your cousin. I am Joel." Joanne got a text from an unknown number.

"Hello," Joanne replied.

"How are you?" Joel asked.

"I am good. If you don't mind, may I know the reason for your message?" she asked.

"Actually, I was the one to whom your cousin gave the form and photos to submit for admission. From there, I saw your photos and I really liked you," he said.

"Thanks," she replied.

"Unfortunately, you got the admission there, but I really hoped you would be coming here. My bad," he said.

"Yeah! I got my admission here," she replied.

"I really like you. I was really hoping you must have joined here," he said.

"Things changed and for my future, it was better here," she replied.

"Ok. Nice talking to you. All the best for your future. Bye. Take care," he said.

"Thank you. Bye, take care," she said.

Joel was a guy from her cousin's college. Her cousin, Mel, and Joel met at the canteen and they had been friends since then. He started texting Joanne on a daily basis. The conversation went on for 15 days and he proposed to her.

Joanne said YES without thinking about anything. She was desperate to have a boyfriend. She did for one more reason; she hoped Leo would get jealous and express his feelings.

She told Leo about Joel, but nothing bothered him much in the beginning.

Eventually, their conversation got less with each other and her phone got busier with Joel more.

Leo felt bad but he was fine.

At first, she thought Leo liked her, but then he moved on and after one year he started dating too.

4

HAZARDOUS HAIRCUT

6 PM

STREET SIDE

NEAR PAYING GUEST

"Hi Joanne! Tell me, how am I looking?" Willow asked.

"It's nice," Joanne replied.

"Tell me seriously!" Willow asked.

"It's not great, but it's okay," Joanne replied.

"I will kill her. Look! How badly did she cut my hair?" Willow said. She burst into tears on the streets where she met Joanne.

"It's okay, Willow. These are just hair, it will grow. Stop crying, please. You don't look good when you cry," Joanne said.

"OK, Joanne. Thank you and love you," Willow said.

Willow and Joanne are PG friends. She was closest to Joanne. She was older than her. They washed their clothes together and waited to eat together. So she treated her like a younger sister.

After 6 months, Joanne shifted to a hostel.

For that hostel, a person has to apply to take admission, so her name was on the waiting list. Finally, she moved there, but she remained in touch with Willow.

Willow stayed in the PG for a year and then she moved to a flat with her friend.

5

NEW STAY

HOSTEL

6:30 AM

"Hello, Joanne," the warden said.

"Hi, warden ma'am. How are you?" Joanne replied.

"Why was your room's light turned on last night?" she asked.

"Ma'am, I was scared to sleep alone," Joanne said.

"Oh! Ok. That's okay," the warden replied.

Everyone had to write the timings of their entry and exit from the hostel in a register. The register is kept at the entrance of the hostel. Joanne got her room next to the warden's room which was a single-seater. The hostel had proper timings for breakfast, lunch, and dinner. It was tough for her in the beginning as she was shy and found it difficult to make friends, but eventually, she got a few people to talk to.

After a month, the warden shifted her to the second floor in three-seaters.

Joanne felt better too. Actually, that room was a standby room, where one person lived there until another girl vacated the hostel.

6

NEW ROOMMATES

3 SEATER ROOM

WINDOW-SIDE BED

9:30 AM

SUNDAY

"Hi. What's your name?" Everly asked.

"Hi. Joanne, and yours?" Joanne replied

"I am Everly, call me eve!" Everly replied.

"In which college are you?" Everly asked.

"City College," Joanne replied.

"Oh! Lots of people are here from that college. You might get friends here," Everly said.

Oh! Ok! That's nice," Joanne replied.

"Do you want to go for breakfast?" Everly asked.

"I will, but after 15 minutes. I will just unpack these," Joanne replied.

"Ok. Then I will go. Bye!" Everly replied.

"Bye!" Joanne answered.

Everly was her new roommate, very simple but the messiest among all. She was older than her. Her study table was covered with dust with the toppings of unarranged books. Her chair looked like a colorful and messy cake which was covered with clothes. And whenever she opened her almirah, her clothes jumped out. Not to forget how messy her bed and mattress were.

Whenever she wanted to study at the study table, she would shift the pile of clothes from chair to bed and whenever she wanted to sleep, she would do the opposite.

Generally, she studied on her messy bed. It was so difficult for her to find anything. But, she had the sharpest memory and was the most talented in the whole hostel. People went to her for solutions to the problems in studies. She cleared CPA in one go. She was a genuine person at heart.

Joanne felt, "Messy and lazy people are extremely talented!"

Her brother was messy too, but extremely talented. She saw two or more people like that. Her brother was great in his studies and got settled on time. She got compared with her brother most of the time.

Joanne's brother was settled with his job.

7

EAT, SNEAK, THEFT, AND DANCE

HOSTEL

6 PM

IN ROOM

"Hey, Joanne! What are you doing?" Anne asked.

"Hi, just doing my class assignments," Joanne replied.

"I am hungry. Let's eat something," Anne said.

"Ok, what do you want to eat? I have some snacks. Wait, I will give them to you," Joanne said.

"Ok, and also let's go to each room and find snacks from other people!" Anne said.

"Oh, seriously. OK," Joanne said. She felt pretty weird thinking that. "Yeah. After that, you are going to show me your dance," Anne said.

"OK," Joanne replied.

Anne was her second roommate. Her bed was in the middle, between Joanne and Everly. She was the eldest among three. She was about to finish her course and leave the hostel in 3 months.

What happened on that day? There was no one on the whole floor, only these two were there. They kept on searching the food from everyone's room and they found something, ate that, and kept the packet back.

After that, Anne played the song and Joanne danced, she loved watching Joanne dance.

It rarely happens that the whole hostel is so empty but on that day it was.

8

HOSTEL FRIENDS

MESS

9 PM

DINNER TABLE

"In which room do you stay?" Shirlia asked.

"4th room, 2nd floor. And you?" Joanne asked.

"3rd floor, first room. Which college and batch?" Shirlia asked.

"City College, Bachelor of Commerce," Joanne replied.

"There are three to four girls from the same college and course, we all can go together. Come! I will introduce you," Shirlia told Joanne.

"Oh! Nice! Yeah! Why not?"

Joanne met everyone and they started to go to college together. She used to wait for Ivy at her usual place and the rest of her hostel friends moved towards their college.

Shirlia and the other girls became very good friends and they ate together, studied together, and shared all their secrets with each other.

Especially during dinner, they would call each other and then go to the mess at the same time. Then they would have long conversations with each other on the terrace and after that, they would go back to their rooms, study, and then sleep.

If anyone's roommate was not there, all four of them would sleep together in one room. They would watch movies together and also play cards.

9

CELL PHONE BATH

Hostel

5:30 AM

MESSAGE BEEPS

"Stay in front of the hostel, I will come, and pick you up!" Ivy texted.

"Ok," Joanne replied and then she went to take a bath.

She took her bucket, cosmetics, clothes, and phone for songs to listen to in the bathroom, as people shared common bathrooms. Everyone had to keep their own bucket to use. As she completed the bath, she took all the things in her hand, including her phone. There was half a bucket of water kept in one corner, the phone slipped from her hand and the phone also took a bath in half a bucket of water.

She came out, got ready, and went outside the hostel to wait for them. As her phone was not working, she went before the scheduled time.

Ivy came with her boyfriend in his car. Joanne sat and even met her boyfriend, Levi. They went together to have breakfast and she opened her phone completely and kept it on the seat of the car.

He dropped them at college and skipped the first class.

It was the first time Joanne met Levi and he was really nice. It became a usual thing for them to skip the first class and go for breakfast together. They have a particular breakfast place where they go and eat. By the end of the year, Joanne, and Ivy's attendance was less.

The parents were called for short attendance. Ivy's mother came and she became an aunt to Joanne too. They were called to complain about attendance, but Ivy's mother supported both of them.

10

HOOOOOK AHHHHHHHHHH

7:30 PM

CAFE

"Hi!" Shirlia called.

"Hello. What are you doing?" Joanne asked.

"Nothing, getting bored. Where are the others?" Shirlia enquired.

"I think they are at their tuition classes," Joanne replied.

"Do you want to go somewhere?" Shirlia asked.

"Yeah. Let's go out, then we will see," Joanne replied.

"Ok, I will get ready and come to your room and then we will go," Shirlia suggested.

"Ok, I will get ready and wait for you," Joanne replied.

Shirlia came to Joanne's room and then they went out. There were so many shops, restaurants, cafes, stalls, and parks outside the hostel.

While roaming around, they saw a cafe and decided to try some snacks there. They went in and ordered snacks to eat.

"Hey, look, they have hookah, wanna try?" Shirlia asked.

"Yeah, okay," Joanne said.

"Your corn cheese balls and hookah are here for you," a waiter came and kept it on the table.

"It's nice, Joanne," Shirlia said.

"Yeah! Even I like it," Joanne replied.

They cleared the checks and decided to leave at 8:45. While leaving and reaching the exit gate, Shirlia felt dizzy.

" What happened? Come and sit, we will go after 5 minutes," Joanne said.

"I think the hookah hit a bit," Shirlia said.

Seeing Shirlia's situation, one of the people in the cafe came and understood the situation. He brought a glass of lemon water which she drank and felt fine after 10 minutes.

"Are you fine now?" Joanne asked. She was worried thinking about how they would go back now.

"Yeah, now I am fine, we can go. Sorry, Joanne," Shirlia said.

"Hey! It's okay. No worries dear. Don't think, let's go now," Joanne said.

They went to the hostel, without having dinner and they slept.

It was an experience for Joanne to handle because it did not hit her much, but then she realized from now on they would go as a group.

She was quite strong. The day ended.

11

6 MONTHS PASSED

Joanne was in a long-distance relationship with Joel. When she started the relationship, it was a casual thing, but slowly she started loving him harder. They started dating each other online only.

"Hi, Joanne," Joel texted.

"Hi. What are you doing?" Joanne replied.

"Nothing, there is a surprise for you!" Joel texted.

"Wow! Tell!" Joanne replied.

"I am planning to come to your city!" Joel texted.

"Hi, Joel! Now, tell me why?" Joanne called him.

He picked up the phone.

"What? Why? What kind of question is this? Just to meet you," Joel said.

"Seriously! When? I am so happy!" Joanne asked happily.

"After 15 days," Joel said.

"I am so happy. When will you book the tickets and how will I recognize you? I always met you virtually," Joanne said.

"I have booked the tickets, sending them to you now, check it! Coming after 15 days!" Joel replied.

"Wear a red colored checked shirt. And I will come to meet you at the station," Joanne said.

"Ok, but I will meet you after going to my friend's place where I am staying. I will freshen up and keep my luggage there. Then I will meet you at your nearest station," Joel said.

"Ok. Happy and excited too! Love you, Joel!" Joanne said.

"Love you too, we will talk later on! Bye, TC," Joel said.

"Bye TC," Joanne replied.

She was extremely excited to meet him and was anxious too. Slowly and slowly, the days passed.

12

15 DAYS LATER

STATION

12 PM

"Hi, Joanne!" Joel kept watching her at first and then he said.

"Hi, Joel." Joanne was extremely nervous and her heart was racing fast.

They hugged each other. She thought he looked great in this simple shirt. Tall, fair, and broad shoulders. The eyes looked like they had something to say and when he spoke, his lips only fluttered like a butterfly. When he even walked, more than a boyish look, he had the grace of a man. For Joanne, he was a dream boy, she felt really blessed to date him.

Joanne wore a simple pair of jeans and a T-shirt, as it was her first time dating, she didn't know how to get ready.

"How was your journey? You must be tired by now," Joanne asked.

"Not much. Slept in train, I am good," Joel said.

"OK. Let's go and eat something. There is a good place near my hostel," Joanne said.

"OK, Let's take a cab then!" Joel said.

"OK," Joanne replied.

They both sat together in a cab. Joanne was feeling great with him.

They both didn't even touch each other as they both were feeling shy.

They reached the restaurant and ordered sandwiches and coffee. They ate looking at each other and then Joel asked, "Is there any place to sit and spend some time?"

"Let's go to the park which I know is really good," Joanne said.

They reached the park. It was a big, nice, beautiful, and peaceful park. Soft romantic songs were being played there. There was a mini cafe inside it, and beside that, there was a place to sit. They went there. They spent their whole day talking. There were benches in between the trees. They sat there for the rest of the day, undisturbed by anyone.

After spending the whole day together, Joel dropped her at the hostel.

He took the local train and went to the place where he stayed.

13

GET TOGETHER

NEXT DAY

IVY'S HOUSE

6 AM

Ivy came down. Joanne and Joel reached there from their place.

"Hi, Joel, and Joanne. Good to see you here, how are you?" Ivy asked.

"Hi. I am good. How are you?" Joel said.

"Good. Good. Levi is here, let's go and have breakfast at our favorite place," Ivy said.

"Yeah!" both said.

Ivy sat in the front with Levi. Joel and Joanne sat behind them.

"Hi Bro," Levi said.

"Hi, Levi. Heard so many things about you and Ivy from her. Finally, I am happy to meet you all," Joel said.

"Oh! That's great. We know each other through Ivy and Joanne. It's really good to see you both together. For how many days are you here?" Levi asked.

"I am here for 15 days. How is your work going on?" Joel replied.

"It is going fine, it's business after all. It has its ups and downs. Well, we all can meet again then when you are here for such a time," Levi said.

"Yeah, sure," Joel said.

Levi ordered their regular famous breakfast, and they both bought it in the car and ate together. Then he dropped them off at college and said he would drop Joel at the nearest station for his home.

Joanne had a busy schedule of tuitions that day, and it turned into a tiring night. They decided not to meet that day after that.

14

GOLDEN DAYS FOR JOANNE

SUNDAY

MOVIE HALL

11 AM

They decided to go on a movie date. Joanne booked the tickets, after that they went to the mall and spent their time together till evening and he dropped her back to the hostel.

One day, he met all of her hostel friends at a cafe. They ordered something, ate, and talked for a while. They went and strolled around everywhere. They had a random fight in between but everything was sorted in an hour.

Roaming and hanging around, those days passed quickly.

15

TIME TO DEPART

15 days passed.

STATION

2 PM

"I will miss you!" Joanne said with teary eyes.

"I will miss more!" Joel said, hiding his feelings behind a smile. "When are you going to come next?" Levi asked.

"No plans yet, but I will make it soon," Joel replied.

"Finish your grad course and come for a job here. Then we all can stay together in the same city," Ivy said.

"Yeah, let's see, I will definitely try," Joel replied.

The train gave the signal and it was time for Joel to leave.

"I had a really good time with you. Please make another plan soon. We will miss you, bro," Levi said.

"Yeah! Sure! I am leaving behind half my heart here! You all are here! I am the one leaving! More than anyone,

I will miss everyone, you all gave me beautiful memories!" Joel said.

"Love you, Joanne," Joel said while hugging her tightly. "I will miss you like hell," he whispered in her ears.

"Love you too," Joanne said and started crying, hoping that he could stay for some more time.

Joel hugged Ivy and Levi too.

Everyone waved goodbye.

His train went off.

This is how they kept on meeting. Sometimes, Joel would come every 6 months to meet or within a year. They spent most of the time together and for Joanne, it was like her golden days as he made her feel special.

Joel shifted for 6 months to Joanne's city and searched for a job there after graduation. They spent their time together on weekends. But after 6 months, he didn't find much growth in his career and went back to the same city.

Joanne felt alone. She continued with her studies and her exam time showed up for professionals. She started working hard for it.

And the exam finished.

16

ALONE! LOST! FAILED!

NEXT MORNING

HER DAY STARTED AS USUAL!

Joanne missed Joel a lot! She was feeling extremely drained and was also chatting with Joel. She was missing him a lot.

She said to herself, "Long-distance relationships are tough," and she went to get ready for college.

She went to college and other classes and went back to the hostel feeling very lethargic and was lying on her bed. Shirlia entered the room.

"What happened with your competitive result?" Shirlia asked.

"Oh shit! I completely forgot to check it. I will check now," Joanne replied.

"Let's check together and see," Shirlia said.

"Yeah! Here is the roll number," Joanne said.

She entered the roll number.

"You didn't clear it, you are short by just 6 marks. Sorry Joanne," Shirlia said.

"It's okay. What about you and the others?" Joanne asked.

"I passed. Everyone cleared except Paige. But don't worry, you will clear it next time and you really worked hard," Shirlia said.

"Congratulations! Thank you Shirlia for encouraging me," Joanne said.

"Thank you, Joanne. I will go now and meet you at the dinner table."

OK," Shirlia said.

"Yeah. Bye," Joanne said.

"Bye. Please don't be upset, I am there for you," Shirlia told her.

"I know, Shirlia. Go now, we will meet in a while," Joanne said.

"Hmm," Shirlia said and went into her room.

Joanne felt like a loser. She lay on her bed again and was crying slowly. No one was there in the room at that time.

Then slowly she slept and didn't have dinner either.

Everyone consoled her, but she felt like a loser.

She took the same exam again after 6 months. She fell short once again by a few marks.

It kept on shattering her confidence, she kept on trying.

She took another competitive exam and that time she cleared it in one go.

END OF 1 YEAR.

When she kept on failing in her life, she remembered one line that her uncle had told her.

"As expected, you won't be able to do anything in life." That line ignited her more to prove him wrong. The uncle was really strict about studies and discipline, but children like Joanne were unable to cope with him. She was not very intelligent and he always asked basic questions to her in front of everyone. She would not be able to answer them which embarrassed her even more.

Joanne's cousins were really doing well and she kept on flunking really well.

THINGS MOVED ON!

17

GROUP STUDY

HOSTEL

5:30 PM

JOANNE'S ROOM

"Hey! When are you going to study?" Paige said.

"Will start now!" Joanne said.

"Where are the others?" Paige asked.

"Maybe in their rooms," Joanne said.

"Ok! Let's go and see what the others are doing! Paige said.

"Ok! Let's go," Joanne said.

Paige is one of Joanne's four group buddies from the hostel. She shared the same floor with her and they got stuck with a competitive exam together, but later she cleared the next exam. They were like close buddies, sometimes they shared the bed in Joanne's room. When they fought, it would become so bad that they wouldn't even talk for a week. But they cared for each other like sisters.

Paige and Joanne went to Shirlia's room just to discuss the exams.

"Hello, Shirlia! Have you started preparing?" Paige asked.

"Just 15 minutes back! Read 3-4 pages," Shirlia said.

"Ok!" Paige said, turning the pages of her book.

"It's all the same. Let's study together," Paige suggested.

"Good idea! We can do that," Shirlia said.

"Yeah! Let's text Penny to come to the third floor," Joanne said.

Penny was the fourth one of her hostel buddies and she lived on the first floor. She came.

"Hey! How did you know that we were in Shirlia's room? I did not mention the room!" Joanne asked.

"Where will you all go if it is the third floor, I know that!" Penny said. Everyone laughed.

"So, where we all will study together as we cannot study in anyone's room. Shirlia, Penny, and I are in three-seaters and Paige in five-seater." Joanne asked.

"In my lobby," Shirlia said.

"Ok. Let's meet there in 5 minutes," Paige said.

Everyone went to bring their books and gathered in the lobby.

"Ok. Now, how to start?" Joanne asked.

"You read one paragraph and explain it," Paige said.

"HA-HA-HA. I will do everything. Ok. Will try," Shirlia said.

"Let's start then," Joanne said.

They all started preparing for the exams together and took a bath around 12 PM and also had lunch in between!

This is how they cleared the whole grads course and 3 years passed!

Joanne cleared the second level of the competitive exam in one go but then she got stuck in a few papers which were easy. She cleared the hardest ones easily.

She tried but then she wondered if she should drop it as it kept on shattering her confidence. But then she thought she should give it one last attempt considering she had invested a lot of time in competitive exams.

18

ARE YOU PREGNANT?

10:30 AM

DOCTOR VISIT

"Hi, doctor," Joanne said.

"Hi, Joanne. How are you?" the doctor asked.

"Good. Thank you! How are you?" Joanne replied.

"Good! Good! Thank you! Tell me, what is your problem?" the doctor asked.

"I have not had my period in four months," Joanne told the doctor.

"Are you pregnant?" asked the doctor instantly.

"No! Not at all!" Joanne replied. She felt horrible suddenly.

"These are the tests and ultrasound, you have to take it. Come and meet me after the tests have been done. I can tell you what is going on once the reports come," the doctor said.

"Ok," Joanne replied.

Joanne went home and the next morning she went to take the test. She got the reports in the evening and went to see the doctor again. She was thinking, "Why did the doctor ask me if I was pregnant? It was so disgraceful. I haven't had sex till now. I am a virgin, even though I have a boyfriend." It kept bothering her for a week.

"You have cystic ovaries because of which you are not getting your periods," the doctor told her.

"Is this a matter of serious concern?" Joanne asked.

"Not now! But during pregnancy, it will be," he said.

"What should I do then?" Joanne worriedly asked.

"Reduce your weight, don't get stressed, and maintain a healthy lifestyle. But for now, I am giving you some medicine."

"Ok," Joanne replied.

"You are good to go. For now, start these medicines, and slowly things will be fine. This is how you have to take the medicines," he said.

"Ok," Joanne said.

"Visit me after one month to track your progress," the doctor said.

"Thank you and bye," Joanne said.

"Bye, Joanne, and take care. Don't worry!" the doctor said reassuringly.

"Yeah! Sure doctor!" Joanne replied.

She left for the hostel and started taking the medicine, but she couldn't reduce the level of stress.

Joanne was an overthinker and a sensitive person. Any small thing would hurt her a lot and it pinched her heart away. This topic kept bothering her for a week and the days passed.

She got her periods after the medicine started and after one month, she visited the doctor again.

Sometimes her periods came on time but sometimes it came after two or three months, this became a regular thing for her. Certainly, she could do everything but couldn't stop stressing out because of her studies, professional exams, and relationship, which deeply impacted her in all aspects.

Joanne really wondered,

"In life, everything is co-related, if your relationship is good, then you can focus on your career more and all in all you will remain happy which in turn will give you better health. If your career is good, even if your relationship sucks, at some point a person will focus on the career again and that might help them be successful."

But, Joanne was losing it all. It was the toughest time for her.

She started a part-time job and also took a professional exam, but she didn't clear it.

She did her part-time job for a few months only.

19

BREAKUP

SUNDAY

10 AM

HOSTEL

"Hi, Joanne," Joel called and said.

"Hi, Joel. What are you doing?" Joanne asked.

"Nothing much. I have to tell you something!" Joel said.

"Say! What happened? Is everything fine?" Joanne asked.

"Everything is fine. I can't continue this relationship any further," Joel said.

"What? You are kidding! I know!" Joanne said.

"No! I am serious, Joanne," Joel said.

"But! Why? Have I done something? Don't say it like this!" Joanne cried.

"I have to focus on my career now! I can't continue this anymore!" Joel said.

"So, when did I become the problem in your career?" Joanne kept crying and asking.

"It's just that I cannot continue it!" Joel said.

"Whatever I have done, I am sorry for that!" Joanne said.

"I don't like your face either. Please stop calling me! It's over!" Joel said.

"What? Why? What is the problem with my face?" Joanne asked.

"Nothing! Bye," Joel said so that Joanne stopped calling him.

"No! No! No! Don't cut the call! What have I done? I will improve myself!!" Joanne kept crying and saying.

"Bye! All the best!" Joel said and hung up the phone.

Joanne kept calling him but he didn't pick it up!

She kept on messaging him to not end the relationship, but he never replied.

She kept calling him on a daily basis. Sometimes he picked up the call and sometimes he ignored it.

She kept on messaging him, but he kept ignoring her.

One day, his phone got busy, and then it got busy on a daily basis.

Frustratingly, he received her call and said, "Stop calling or else I will block you!"

She was broken and shattered and stopped calling him as she understood that he had started dating someone else.

Joanne started losing it all. Her confidence was at an all-time low. She started hating and criticizing herself.

She realized, "Ignorance is the worst thing ever".

She stayed there for a year. She kept writing professional exams, but she kept failing. Her health deteriorated and she started having PCOD, her confidence kept hitting rock bottom and she kept free-falling deeper and deeper.

A year passed!

She decided to go back to stay with her parents and finally decided to stop attempting the competitive exams.

PART -THIRD

DISASTROUS PHASE

Joanne's mother literally wanted her to settle in life! She asked her to take the courses that she preferred like interior or events, as Joanne was extremely creative. She inherited that quality from her mother and she loved to decorate the house or surprise people creatively.

She decided to take event courses in some good city and took admission. For a few days, she went to the classes. But when she had to go to different places for an on-site experience, her mind started playing with her and she plunged into the game of confidence. It started to tear her like hell. She wondered how she would go to different places and how to travel by bus and so on. She was struggling with so many things that every day it became a huge task for her.

She decided to drop out again and look for a job instead! She stayed with one of her older PG friends, Willow. Joanne made a CV and applied to many places online. Her troubled mind didn't let her settle anywhere. She had lots of questions in her mind, like:

Will I be able to do a 9 to 5 job?

I am a loser and failure, I don't know anything!

What if I am unable to operate the lift and coffee machines, and everyone starts laughing?

What if I say the wrong things in a group?

She had all the negative questions but no answers.

She was living in an apartment with her friend and her friend's brother.

She could see office buildings straight away from her room! Every morning, when she woke up, she would see everyone getting ready for the office, it scared her. Even the building acted like a monster, as if it kept on laughing at her shattered life.

She was living in the city where her ex-boyfriend was living. She wanted to patch up with him but he had moved on. He met her just to be intimate and to shatter her. He didn't even want her to stay in the same city.

She was unable to understand anything and was struggling with everything so hard that she returned home. But she really wanted to do something in her life but more than any battle of her career, it was her mind that kept playing with her and situations were already not working in her favor.

There was one thing with Joanne, she knew to fight, work hard, and be hopeful in all the worst cases. She had a big fascination towards her career. Every time she failed, she would quit once but she would also try harder the next. She was unclear with her mind, kept on hustling and bustling, an average holder, but slowly she got inclined to writing.

Writing worked as a therapy for her. Whenever she felt sad, broken, or tired, she would write a poem or journal or write a short story. This was a space where no one judged, laughed, or cared. It was just her and her diary as it liberated her from her thoughts.

Eventually, she got passionate about writing and decided to be a writer!

After all the failures, she didn't give up on HOPE!

She decided to make a name for it and it was just a thought. She tried to publish some of her raw poems which were rejected instantly. The fact was she really needed to work on her writing part!

1

RETURNED HOME

HOME

ROOM

"What are you doing, Joanne? Don't you have to study something?" her mother asked.

"TV Mum! Yeah! Going!" Joanne replied.

She switched off the TV and went into her room.

Joanne's mother knew about the exams and health, but she didn't share about the relationship with her mother, Joanne wasn't sure how her mother would take it.

She kept on struggling with her emotions all alone!

"How is your preparation going on?" Mother came into the room and asked.

"It's good, Mum!" Joanne replied.

"Why don't you enroll in some courses with it, like any grads? You will have a degree with it!" Mother said.

"Yeah, Mom! Nice idea! I will apply here only!" Joanne replied.

She took admission there and thought of attempting professional exams again.

As the results came in, she kept failing the exams. She was losing it all so she decided to stop attempting professional exams once again.

This time she bid her final goodbye to professional exams.

2

ZERO CONFIDENCE

HOME

ROOM

12:00 PM

"Why are you wasting your time by doing nothing, Joanne? Even if you fail, you have to fight again!" Mother said.

Joanne and her mother were lying in bed in the afternoon.

"Yeah!" Joanne said while thinking about quitting.

"Till then, apply here only somewhere in a school or in offices!" Mother said.

"Ok, mom. I made a CV earlier, so I will give it a try!" Joanne said.

Joanne had zero confidence then. Deep within she was thinking,

"Who will hire me?"

"I am such a dumb ass."

"I am good to work somewhere like a maid."

"I am good for nothing, I am dependent on my parents. I am not independent and I keep sucking their money instead of helping. At my age, people are doing jobs."

She kept on questioning herself and was left with hopelessness.

AT NIGHT

"Hey Joanne, I saw an advertisement on Facebook that a school is hiring a teacher. Go to that school tomorrow and take your CV with you!" Mother said while doing some kitchen chores.

"Ok, Mom," Joanne said.

She kept 3-4 copies of her CV on the table and made up her mind that she would go to school and apply!

Then they had dinner and everyone slept after that.

3

HUNTING

SCHOOL

10 AM

NEXT DAY

"Hi! I am here to apply for a job as a teacher, so do you have any vacancies?" Joanne enquired.

"Yeah! We are hiring currently! This is a form you can fill out and submit or you can email it!" Ms Susianna from the front desk said. "Can I fill the form now and submit it?" Joanne asked.

"Yeah! Sure! It's up to you," Ms Susianna said.

"Ok. Thank you!" Joanne said.

She filled out the form and submitted it right away.

"We will contact you for the interview. I hope you mentioned your contact number here," Ms Susianna said.

"Yeah. It's in the form," Joanne said.

"Ok. Till then enjoy your vacay mode before getting hired!" Miss Susianna said.

"HA-HA. Thank you! Take care!" Joanne said.

"You too!" replied Miss Susianna.

Joanne applied to various schools and she went home, deep inside she wanted to work somewhere, she really liked the vibe of the first school.

In the evening, she got a call from that school for an interview to be conducted the very next day with a demo after that!

4

INTERVIEW

NEXT DAY

SCHOOL

9 AM

"Hi! I have been called for an interview today!" Joanne said.

"Hey! Hi! Yeah! Please wait for prayer to finish and then Mr. Sanders will take an interview. You can take a seat till then," Miss Susianna said.

"Ok! Thank you!" Joanne said.

Joanne sat on a chair in the visitors area and waited for the prayer to be over.

After 15 minutes, she was called into the office and she went inside.

"May I come in, Mr. Sanders?" Joanne said.

"Yes and have a seat," Mr. Sanders said.

"Thank you! How are you?" Joanne said.

"I am good, Thank you! How are you?" Mr. Sanders asked and kept scrolling through her CV.

He asked the basic questions, about school, college, and so on and asked questions related to situations involving kids and checked the knowledge. The interview went really well for Joanne, then she was asked to give a demo to teach a lower section class a poem while explaining.

She taught it so well that she was happy about herself. She felt good inside and she went home.

The next day, she got a call and was told that she had been selected for the post of teacher in the lower class as she was a fresher. But still, she was happy with it because she also wanted to work somewhere.

The school which she applied for was new and it was in a developing phase. The school had only up to the 2nd standard when she applied. But in the next 5 years, it extended till the 5th standard. She really liked Mr. Sanders as he was very understanding and he was the owner of that school.

5

TEACHER

NEXTDAY

SCHOOL

LKG CLASS

8 AM

"You have been assigned to handle the LKG class and you will be teaching English. You will also be their class teacher," Miss Susianna said.

"Ok," Joanne said.

She entered the class, introduced herself, and asked the students their names one by one. Someone came in and told each and everything about the students, syllabus, and class.

She struggled a lot the first 15 days with some irritating parents complaining all the time. Then slowly after seeing her pattern of teaching, everyone adjusted. She taught very creatively, did anchoring, conducted activities, and became a favorite among the students and the staff as well. She excelled at her work. She also started writing something on a daily basis before going to sleep. Slowly, she started to heal.

Though she wasn't earning much and wasn't settled like everyone else, she had the satisfaction that she was helping her parents with her presence. Slowly but steadily, her confidence started to develop.

Mr. Sanders was the best person to work with for Joanne as he gave her the freedom to be herself, just like her mother.

6

REGULARS

HOME

LIVING ROOM

10 AM

Everyone was sitting on the couch and watching a movie. Between that, her parents started talking about some things about the shop. Her father got very angry and started to yell at her mother. This continued for half an hour.

Joanne got very worried seeing that. After seeing everything, she realized that her father was wrong somewhere. In the heat of the moment, she went near her father and raised her hand to slap him. But she realized it was wrong and she put her hand down.

She felt guilty about it and her father didn't talk to her for a week.

All in all, her fault was that she couldn't see her mother unhappy and any injustice done to her.

Things became normal with time and slowly her father's anger started to melt away.

Family fights, her shattered career, and her insecurities made her life really difficult to handle.

7

15 YEARS OF FRIENDSHIP

Cynthia and Joanne had been friends for over 15 years. After the first 7 years of friendship, they became friends with a new classmate named Andrew. It was a casual friendship with him for the first 6 years. When Joanne returned to her hometown, Cynthia returned as well since she too was not so successful in her career. From that point onwards, Andrew, Cynthia, and Joanne became very close. Every now and then, they planned to meet at each other's house. They shared secrets with each other. Andrew had a relationship with one of their school friends and he got rejected when he asked her to get married to him. That is how Cynthia and Andrew became closer. He shared each and everything with her. We became survivors of the worst situation for him. He started considering Cynthia like a sister and started liking Joanne. Joanne liked him but not as a boyfriend. Andrew proposed but she rejected. Things went along normally between them despite all of that. Andrew was the most helpful guy. Whenever one of their families had an issue, he stood tall like a wall to fight for them. These three go together everywhere

Some years passed. Cynthia and Andrew's bond grew stronger and Joanne was left behind. Joanne and Cynthia's birthdays have a gap of just 15 days. Andrew celebrated Cynthia's birthday grandly at his home. Joanne watched everything and stayed quiet, but it wounded her badly. She cried a lot when she saw that he gave his attention only to Cynthia and ignored her. Eventually, she distanced herself from both of her friends and started doing everything alone. She met them occasionally but she never shared much.

She felt shattered that her 15 years of friendship now had some linings in it. Whether it's friendship or relationship, it hurts if it has some pain in it. It kept her wounded for a long time.

8

ALEJANDRO

Joanne was 27 and slowly her friends were getting married. One day, she was attending one of her school friend's wedding, and she was scrolling through Facebook. Suddenly, a message popped up on messenger from a complete stranger.

"Hey! Hi! How are you? I know you!" the stranger messaged.

"Hi! I am good. Who is this?" Joanne replied.

"Charlie, Amelie, Ellie – these were the girls from your hostel," the stranger said.

"Yeah! So? How do you know them?" Joanne replied.

"We were in the same class but I never saw you," the stranger replied.

"They are all older than me," Joanne replied.

"OH! That is why! So, where are you these days?" the person asked.

Joanne scrolled through his profile and checked everything about him on Facebook! He looked really good. The stranger's name was Alejandro, which she saw on his profile.

"Why should I really tell you that? Who are you to know all this?" Joanne replied.

"See, there is no loss in chit-chatting and being friends. After all, I am not going to come to your house!" Alejandro said.

"Yeah! Yeah! Let's see!" Joanne replied.

"So, where are you these days? What are you doing?" Alejandro asked.

"I am living with Mum and Dad at their place in their city. Came to one of my friend's weddings and was thinking of giving him a gift. I want to give it to him but the place is filled with people out there," she replied.

"So go and give, did you eat anything at the wedding or not?" Alejandro replied.

"I will eat after giving this. What are you doing?" Joanne asked.

"Coincidentally, I am also at the wedding of one of my cousins in another city," Alejandro said.

"Oh! That's nice! What are you doing these days?" Joanne asked.

"Nothing much! Just office work and home," Alejandro replied.

"Aren't you in touch with anybody from the hostel?" Joanne asked.

"Not now! Earlier I was. Everyone got married now," Alejandro said.

"Ok, nice. When will you come back from the wedding?" Joanne asked.

"I will be late, let's see, what about you? Are you alone?" Alejandro replied.

"In an hour, I think so. I am with friends," Joanne replied.

"It was really nice talking to you. Will talk later on! Bye! Take care!" Alejandro said.

"Same here, Bye. Take care," Joanne replied.

He messaged her on a daily basis. Sometimes he used to share his picture while going to the office, sometimes he would send her voice notes of a song. He would request her to send something in a voice note as she was just texting. He insisted that she send something in a voice note and she sent it. He told her that her voice was the sweetest thing he had ever heard. He looked extremely smart in his photos!

They continued chatting and he kept appreciating her. They talked about their families and everything.

Alejandro's parents were no more, he had two more brothers, he was living with them, but later on, he started to live alone.

One day, he proposed to Joanne and she wasn't prepared for it.

Joanne thought, how come such a smart guy approached her? Why? I look so bad, short, sucked in my career, have anxiety, and keep overthinking, I am not earning well either. Then how?

But she wanted to have a relationship as she liked him. She also wanted to make a fresh start. So she told each and everything about her past, career, family, and relationship. It didn't matter to him and they both started having an affair.

They talked throughout the day and also at night when everyone was asleep. She felt he listened to everything. She liked how much he understood her. She made a plan to do a job in the same city where he lived and stay at some rented place. She decided to meet him and tell him this.

She asked her mother for a change in job to that place but didn't leave the school's job. She updated her CV again, applied to some places, and thought of giving it a try and meeting him.

She went back to that place again for a job and new love. So she texted to him:

"I am coming to your city. If I find a job, I will stay there."

"Nice! When?" Alejandro asked.

Joanne shared the details and he replied that he would meet her at the station.

9

DICEY MEETING

Joanne and Alejandro were quite excited to meet each other. Just two days before the meeting, he said he had to go somewhere for his work. He said he would meet her after he got back.

She became very upset, but then she thought, "What matters is we are going to meet." She waited for two days for him to come.

She stayed at Ivy's house where she lived with her better half. Till then, she thought of applying to various places but again, her fear started to haunt her with as many questions as she could think:

I am dumb.

How will I get a job? I don't know anything.

Will I be able to survive in a job?

What if everyone laughs at me?

These questions haunted her so much that she thought she would ask Alejandro to help her when they met.

TWO DAYS LATER!

She met him at CCD wearing simple jeans and a tee. He was waiting outside the cafe wearing a light cream T-shirt and skinny black jeans. He had a full beard and broad shoulders. He looked different in person compared to his photos. He looked smarter in the photos. They just sat and talked about families, journeys, and help for jobs. She didn't like him much in person and Joanne always kept her word no matter what. He dropped her and they both went off separately.

10

KEPT ON TRYING

Alejandro decided to help her with a job and asked her to read all the things which he specified. He talked to some people about her job and also asked her to contact them once on call. She didn't apply anywhere else on her own because she was under confident though she wanted to.

Alejandro had a rented vacant apartment where they both went once and spent intimate times together. But they didn't have sex as Joanne didn't want to do it before marriage, it was just her wish.

He told her to stay at that apartment and to work from there. But Joanne did not want to have frequent visits from him for being intimate because she knew if she stayed here, that would happen.

She simply said, "Let's see how this job thing goes." She waited for fifteen days and kept meeting him, but nothing happened and she decided to go back as she was not feeling good about staying at her friend's place for so long.

Once she got back, she got a call for a job. But by then she did not want to go back so far.

She started to continue her school job and stayed connected with him.

One day, she asked if he was going to marry her and he agreed to it.

11

HAPPY – BREAKUP

Joanne told her mother that she was dating someone. Her mother asked many questions about him. She felt he was not the perfect guy for Joanne.

Joanne hid two things from her parents, "For how long they have been dating, and how they really met."

But for Joanne, their parents decided to meet him.

Coincidentally, her parents were visiting that city to just visit and roam around. When Joanne told them he lived in the same city, they decided to meet him.

She told Alejandro everything. He said, "I won't be there in the city at that time."

She asked Alejandro again to meet her parents after reaching his city.

To which Alejandro said, "I will be out of the city tomorrow."

Joanne insisted, "You have time today, you can come, and meet now!"

Alejandro said, "It's already quite late, it will take time to reach."

Joanne said, "You can try at least. We can sleep late."

Alejandro said, "I am not ready to meet and get married now. I can't."

Joanne kept quiet for a while and said bye and disconnected the call.

Joanne shared this with one of her cousins. The cousin said one good thing to her which cleared things up.

"If he really wanted you, he would have given his best effort to keep you and never miss this opportunity."

Joanne realized maybe he was not the right one to whom she could get married.

When she told her parents, they were not happy to hear it. Her parents didn't want her to get married to him as they were not satisfied with his family background, financial position, and even his house.

When he backed out from meeting her parents, she felt worse on the inside. She tried really hard and even fought for him to convince her parents to meet him once.

After giving it some thought, she decided to move on. She thought, "Maybe he never wanted to marry me. We were not meant to be together."

She dated him for 6 months but she didn't regret it much and was happy after breaking up with him. She felt light after the breakup, maybe that connection wasn't meant for her.

After the first breakup, it took four years to heal. But after the second breakup, it didn't take a single day to heal. She just felt happy.

Sometimes, your inner instinct always tells you the right thing to do, but humans have the habit of going against it and making it worse.

12

REJOINED

Time passed slowly and she started indulging herself in her school work. She was quite happy living with her parents and doing her schoolwork. Gradually, her focus shifted to writing and she wrote something on a daily basis. She started journaling and with that, she started to heal a bit.

Joanne's parents wanted her to marry a good guy. She started meeting a few guys online after making a profile. She started meeting the guys one by one or she would talk on a call. The thing is today's generation wants everything to be perfect. Some said they want good height, good educational background, a good job, or great looks. Some even asked for pictures without make-up. She kept meeting and talking with multiple people. The process was long and completely exhausting for her mind.

After a lot of hassle, her parents asked someone to meet her. They were family friends. She didn't like him in person but on seeing her parents happy, she decided to meet him.

She started chatting, meeting, and so on. But she wasn't happy deep within. She decided to talk to him and discontinue it, but she stopped herself every time because she did not want to disappoint her parents. But a huge fight happened between the families and that in turn ruined the relationship.

All these things went on for four months.

Joanne was happy that this arranged marriage proposal was over but this impacted her mind. She was sad, lost, and shattered because things never worked in her favor.

She questioned herself, "Why do such things keep happening to me!"

Things went on!

13

ONE MORE TRY

Joanne was really good at making friends and she had lots of friends in school. One of them was very close to her. Joanne always wanted to do a job in a big city and be independent. But, she did not have the confidence to do it.

In her workplace, one of her friends was shifting to a new city to start a new job. Joanne asked, "Do you think I could get a job where you are applying?"

Her friend said, "Why not? You can come with me! We will try together. I have my boyfriend there. He will help me and will help you too!"

Joanne thought, "Yeah, there is no surety but let's give it a try!"

She went with her to try one more time to find a job.

But the real hassle was not finding a job, it was where she stayed. She lived in the most pathetic place with her for 15 days. She struggled every single day of it. She lived in the dirtiest place she had ever stayed in. She kept suffering through it all just for a job.

15 days passed.

Every now and then, they would go to the office for interviews and return empty-handed.

Joanne never tried anything on her own, she always needed some support and never really had any patience.

She decided to go back home.

Her friend got the job after applying to some more places. It took more than a month but she finally started earning.

Joanne regretted her decision and started working at the school again.

She stopped thinking about other jobs, focused on her school, and just wanted to get married.

She always had the passion to do something, but did not know how to!

She said to herself, "I will keep on trying till my last breath. Even if I do nothing, I will have peace in my grave because I will know that I tried my best."

Sometimes, she really wondered if maybe God wanted her to do something much bigger in life than a normal job.

I am such a dumb ass, now I can just hope.

14

REGULAR HI'S

One day, she got a text from a guy on an online site saying, "Hi".

She got into his profile and checked everything. His profile name was John. He looked good. The smile on his face was like a gentle breeze which soothed his face. He was fair, smart, and an extremely simple guy. She thought it would be like her other relations and other regular hi's and then she took it casually. She texted him, "Hi!"

Joanne was searching for a guy on an online app.

He asked, "How are you?"

She replied, "I am good. How are you?"

He texted, "Good! Let's connect on call tomorrow at 5 PM."

She replied, "Can we connect at 5:30 if you don't mind? I will be out at that time."

He texted, "Sure! Ok bye. Take care!"

She replied, "Thank you! Bye! Take care!" The day ended casually.

The next day, she got a Whatsapp call from his no. at 5:30.

She had just come from somewhere and went straight to her room to talk to him.

"Hi. How are you?" he asked.

"Good. What about you? What were you doing?" she asked.

"Good! Just ended my office call and called you. What were you doing?" he enquired.

"Just came back from the market," she said.

"Oh, nice! So, what do you do?" he asked.

"Well, I teach 5th graders. Where are you these days?" she asked

"Nice. I am with my parents in my hometown for a few days," he said.

"What is your job profile?" she asked.

"Finance Manager.What do you do as a job?" he said.

"I teach 5th graders, English as a subject, certainly their class teacher too." she said

"Good!What's your favorite food?" he asked.

"Well! Good timing. I am eating right now. Chinese. What's yours?" she replied.

The conversation went on for more than an hour or so. It was the smoothest conversation in her life. They talked about their likes and dislikes, families, jobs, marriage, and everything.

It was a deep conversation. She never felt that way before. She felt so calm from the inside that she had the deepest sleep for the first time in her whole life. With one call, it washed away all her anxieties and overthinking.

The day she saw his photo, she wanted to marry him despite not knowing much about him. And the day she spoke to him, she only got sure about it. After that, they decided to meet each other.

Every time they decided to meet, something happened, and it got cancelled. They got a chance to meet after three whole months.

They decided to meet at a cafe and had a super casual meeting. Then they decided to meet one more time and talked to each other about everything.

They dated for 9 months. It was tough for Joanne to understand him fully because he spoke less. He didn't share much and never dated anyone in his whole life. He didn't know how to be in a relationship and how to express his feelings. Still, Joanne liked him a lot and she was crazy about him.

Sometimes, huge fights also happened between them. But he had a lot of patience and spoke less. He was also a good listener. He used to take her to the park, for long drives, coffee dates, beer dates, and so on.

One day, he confessed his feelings to her and proposed to her. Joanne was already worried that he might lose interest in her.

Joanne was happy hearing this and she said yes.

After some time, they got married to each other.

15

LIFE CHANGED FOREVER

Little Joanne remained the same with the height but her problem of anxiety, overthinking, and negativity for herself started to melt away slowly after meeting him. She went too far from her world to a new country, where he loved her like no one else did. He treated her like a princess, supported her dreams, and they stayed in a cottage-type dream house. Coincidentally, whatever Joanne saw in romantic movies was really fulfilled by him unknowingly.

They had huge fights and things were not easy but when she worked on herself, she knew how she could handle the problems positively. It was tough to make him understand the importance of communication, talking, sharing feelings, listening when she needed to cry and understand, pouring her heart out, and consoling her when she was crying.

She realized that every relationship was a two-way task. When God puts two persons together, there is a reason behind that, to heal one another. He didn't know how to love himself either, how to communicate, and share feelings, to make buddies etc.

He gave unconditional love, passed no judgments, pampered her like a princess, let her do what she wanted, shopped for her, and cared for her parents as well. They both evolved and worked together to make the relationship work.

She changed her whole routine of habits like sleeping on time, exercising, meditation, eating healthy food, praying, journaling, etc. She worked hard and healed herself. It took more than a year for her to heal.

She started to work on her novel as an amateur, worked day in, and out for a year and published it.

Soon, she conceived after a year, had a baby, published another novel and became a writer.

After so much suffering, she never gave up the hope to work for her dreams and continued to strive for it and get what she wanted for herself.

For Joanne,

She was criticized her whole life either for her height, looks, or education. She lost her self-worth and confidence. She became a completely negative person.

Whenever she speaks something, she would speak negatively about herself. She stopped seeing any positivity in her life and attracted more negativity. She had judgmental people all around her who every now and then judged her, mocked her, criticized her, and talked negatively about her. It became more difficult for her to bloom as she was already suffering with her life earlier.

But, one right person, at the right place, and at the right time healed her completely.

She changed her way of seeing herself and started loving herself which turned out to be a life changer for her. She only spoke positively in every situation, even during the worst possible situations.

She was at that place where no one judged her or doubted her. In return, she bloomed perfectly.

HOW DID JOANNE KEEP HERSELF POSITIVE AGAINST ALL THE ODDS?

When Joanne flunked, she always said to herself, "There are many great persons who did well in her life after flunking in 12th." Obviously, it was a tough year, but she kept on fighting.

When Joanne failed professional courses, she kept on reminding herself, "Maybe God wanted me to do something great in life." Still, she used to have doubts about herself all the time after that.

When she saw her family fight a lot, she reminded herself, "Maybe God wanted to keep me strong in all the situations."

When she got dumped, she was an extremely weak person emotionally. She started becoming emotionally strong.

When she got ditched by friends for whom she had done a lot, she understood God wanted her to break all her boundaries of fear. At first, it hurt her obviously, but after some time she made herself understand.

When she was not able to find a job, she said to herself, "Maybe I will do something great in life."

Every now and then, God gives us tough situations about which we cry and crib a lot. But that always teaches us to stay strong.

You will never understand it when a particular situation happens. But when you give it time, you will get to know why God put us through it.

If these situations never come, then she would never have become this strong.

"THE HABIT OF NEVER GIVING UP,

THINKING POSITIVELY IN THE WORST SITUATION,

TRUST IN GOD AND HOPE

LEAD

JOANNE

TO DO SOMETHING

IN HER LIFE.

A JOURNEY IS NEVER EASY,

FULL OF SELF DOUBT

TOUGH SITUATIONS

BUT THERE COMES ALONG

SELF DETERMINATION

AND

TIMING OF GODS AND ANGELS.

I HEARD THIS LINE IN A MOVIE,

"IF YOU REALLY WANT SOMETHING IN LIFE FROM THE HEART,

THE WHOLE WORLD CONSPIRES TO OFFER

IT TO YOU."